MICKEY THE BEAVER

and other stories

"That's Our Cheep" page 25

MICKEY THE BEAVER

"The Blind Deer" page 55

Illustrated by Audrey Teather

BY KERRY WOOD

and other stories

"Mickey the Beaver" page 1

1964
MACMILLAN OF CANADA
TORONTO

Printed in Canada for The Macmillan Company of Canada Limited, 70 Bond Street, Toronto, by the T. H. Best Printing Company Limited.

NOTE

Doris Forbes, the girl who cared for Mickey the beaver, asked me to help her write the first story in this book; she told me everything that happened and I wrote it down for her as if she were telling it herself. In the other stories, about a robin and a deer, I am writing about my own experiences.

KERRY WOOD

MICKEY THE BEAVER

MICKEY THE BEAVER

My pet beaver, Mickey, came to us by accident. It was in June of 1939 that we got him. Lots of beavers were living in Waskasoo Creek, which flows past our house at Red Deer, Alberta, but some men were breaking the law by trapping them at night and we think Mickey's mother was caught and killed. A high-school girl named Jean Yuill found Mickey on the sidewalk near our house one June morning on her way to school. The tiny beaver kitten was hurt. He couldn't move his hind legs at all, and his

back was all scratched and bleeding, and it looked as though a cat had mauled him.

Jean carried him over to my Dad, who was out in the garden. Dad brought him into the house to Mother, and as Mother had been a nurse she knew how to fix up the cuts. When Mother and Dad had looked after his wounds, they wondered what they could feed him. Mother heated some milk, and Dad held a spoon against the animal's mouth while Mother poured milk into the spoon. The little beaver got the idea right away, being very hungry. He put up his front paws, which looked like hands, and one grabbed the spoon handle while the other hung on to the

end of the spoon. He drank and drank until his stomach swelled up tight. Then he lay down to sleep, so Dad found a shoe-box and Mother padded it with soft cloths, and they put him under the stove where it was warm.

I came home from school at noon and that was the first time I saw him. He didn't have a name then, but I called him Mickey straight off. I knew right away that I wanted Mickey for a pet, and Mother let me help feed him and look after his hurts. Dad went up-town and saw Sergeant Matheson of the R.C.M.P., and this policeman said it was all right for us to have Mickey. Beavers belong to the government, so a person needs permission to keep one. I found out later that Sergeant Matheson and my Dad and Mother didn't think Mickey would live, but I knew he would.

We looked after him as well as we could, and in three days the paralysis went out of his back legs and a week later his back and shoulder cuts closed up. By this time he was friendly with all of us. He had tried to nip Mother the first hour while she was doctoring him, but after that he never wanted to bite anyone. He soon learned his name and waddled across the floor whenever I called him. We estimated his age at about four weeks when we got him. He was then ten inches long, counting his tail. He could sit on my hand, easily. Fully-grown, he measured forty-four inches and weighed seventy pounds.

We didn't know what to feed Mickey at first. Mother thought milk was the best food for a baby beaver, and Mickey thought so too. We tried other things, though. Dad gathered clover leaves

and willow twigs and poplar bark, and Mickey nibbled on them. We even tried to feed him hamburger, until we learned that beavers don't eat meat. I guess Mickey didn't know this, because he ate some. He liked bread better, and bread and milk was his favourite dish at first. Later we found out that he was fond of fruit and would eat any kind at all. A box of apples lasted him a month. Twenty-five cents worth of bananas lasted him two days. He took hold of fruit with both front paws, holding it up against his mouth and making a funny little *mew* sound like a baby, because he was happy.

Well, the news soon got around that we had a baby beaver at our house, and every person in Red Deer wanted to see Mickey. One Sunday in July, soon after we got him, fifty people came at different times from morning until night just to see him. Dad hunted out a large pan and filled it full of water from the creek, and Mickey thought that was swell. He climbed in and paddled around, having a grand time. The Waskasoo Creek is only a hundred feet from our house, and we took him there often. Mickey swam in the creek, but never went far from us. There were other beavers living in the creek and often we'd see them, and Mickey acted as if he was scared of them. Anyway, he always came out and waddled after us whenever we started for home.

Papers printed stories about our having a pet beaver, and people from out-of-town started coming to see him too. A couple of tourists all the way from Switzerland were staying at Banff; they heard about Mickey and came the 200 miles to Red Deer

just to see him. Mrs. Bloch-hiller – that was the lady's name – gave me a beautiful Swiss purse as a present when I gave her a picture of Mickey, and Mr. Bloch-hiller gave me some real Swiss chocolate, which Mickey and I ate and liked.

Later in the summer, Mr. and Mrs. Wendell Chapman of Los Angeles, California, came to Red Deer with their big trailer and stayed at the auto-camp while they took hundreds of pictures of Mickey and me. They took moving pictures as well as ordinary ones. Later, they sold some of the movies to Hollywood film companies, and Mickey was shown on the movie news. The Chapmans took Mother and Dad and Mickey and me out to Sylvan Lake in their car, and Mickey loved that. Sylvan Lake is a resort fifteen miles from Red Deer, and I took my bathing-suit and went in swimming with Mickey. He would swim away out into the lake until he got tired, then turn and come to me and mew until I picked him up in my arms to give him a little rest. While at Sylvan Lake we fed Mickey an ice-cream cone, and it was funny to see him eat it. The ice cream melted and dripped over his fur. Mickey tried to lick it off and set up a funny wailing cry because he was worried about getting his fur messy and also worried about losing the ice cream. Mickey was very clean and spent a lot of time combing out his fur with the big claws on the inside of his two hind legs. He didn't like to be dirty, not even for a little while.

My Dad dug a big hole in the backyard and we filled it full of water. While it was still fresh, I used to go in swimming with

Mickey there. He'd dive into the deep part and tickle my toes and make me jump. But soon he got the pool all cluttered up by carrying in sticks and by digging at the sides, so I had to keep out of it and leave him there alone. People liked to see him swim and liked to look at his flat tail and his big webbed hind feet, which he used when swimming. He could swim very fast.

When school started again after the summer holidays, the teacher asked me to bring Mickey to school one Friday afternoon to show the others. I carried Mickey to school with me and showed him to all the pupils in my class, as well as to the pupils in four other classrooms. They asked a lot of questions about what he ate and what he did, and all the Grade I pupils came up to the front in single file and patted Mickey and touched his tail. Mickey didn't mind.

That first winter we didn't quite know what to do with Mickey. We had a garage which we didn't use and we kept him locked up there during the day. Mickey slept all day until around five o'clock in the afternoon, unless we wakened him to meet visitors. Dad built him a warm kennel and put it in the garage, and supplied poplar and willow logs for him to chew on, and Mickey was happy there. When he woke up at five on winter days, he'd bang on the garage doors until Mother or Dad or I went and got him and brought him into the house. We let him play in the house until our bedtime; then we put him back in the garage. He played there until nearly dawn when he went into his kennel and fell asleep.

We had to teach him not to chew our house furniture. At first it was difficult, because he had sharp teeth and loved gnawing on wood, but we tried to teach him that we needed the furniture for ourselves. He used to take sticks out of the wood-box and stack them on the kitchen floor, but that got too messy and we coaxed him to use old slippers instead. He would line up the slippers as if barring off part of the floor to make a dam across

the kitchen. Out in the garage he shifted his logs around every night, sometimes piling them in a corner like a beaver house, sometimes making a dam across the garage floor. He was awfully strong and could move our fifty-pound kitchen table easily, just by dragging it with his teeth clamped on one leg. Once, when Mother had to go uptown and left Mickey alone in the kitchen, he piled the big table, three chairs, a stool, and a smaller table tight against the outside door, and Mother couldn't get inside when she came home.

The first winter, the Alberta Natural History Society held a meeting at our house one night to meet Mickey. We had a good time and Mickey behaved just fine. He had a wrestle with Dad, sat up and begged for food from Mother, and let me take him around for each member of the club to pet. He even climbed onto the laps of some of the lady members, which seemed to scare them just a little. Mickey weighed forty pounds then. The Natural History Society made Mickey and the rest of our family honorary members of their club, and we began going to their meetings. Each member brought Mickey a present that night, and someone must have told them what he liked. There were canned peaches, canned pears, canned apricots, dried apricots, bunches of carrots, lettuce, and even a few bottles of pickles – Mickey loved pickles! Mr. G. N. Finn, who was president of the society at that time, made a nice speech and thanked our family for taking in this orphaned beaver and giving him a good home.

Mickey froze his tail in February that winter. He came in from

the garage one morning, mewing loudly. The tail was frozen solid, and we were all worried and didn't know what to do. But Mickey himself knew. He got hold of his tail and started to massage it, beginning at the base and working towards the tip. Mother said he was restoring the circulation. He worked on it for hours and hours, and finally the tail got all better and healed up, good as new. After that we kept him inside the house whenever it was very cold outside, but he always banged furniture

around downstairs, so it was hard for us to sleep when he was spending the night indoors.

The same winter I caught whooping cough. Mickey called to visit me in my bedroom every evening, and, the first thing we knew, he'd caught whooping cough too. Mother said it was funny but pathetic to see Mickey sitting up on his hind legs, his front

paws hugged tight around his chest, rocking back and forth while he whooped with the cough. He had a worse case than mine and we all worried about him until he got over it.

When Mickey came to visit me in my bedroom upstairs, Mother would first take the vacuum cleaner and go all over him, to clean him before he climbed up the stairs to my room. Mickey loved being cleaned by the vacuum. When Mother had finished, I would hear him coming slowly upstairs, his heavy tail bumping on each step. I spread a bath-mat on the bed, and Mickey would lie on it and stay quiet while I talked to him and petted him.

A magazine editor asked me to get a picture of Mickey chopping down a tree. Well, Mickey chewed a little on some of the poplar trees near our place, but I don't think he ever chopped one down. Then Mother and I remembered about Mickey liking candy, so we melted some licorice and spread it on a tree-cut that Mickey had nibbled once, and Mickey reared up there and licked at the candy while our photographer friend, Mr. Arthur Keen of Red Deer, took his picture.

Lots of people came to see Mickey. Madame de Gripenberg, wife of the Finnish consul, who was speaking in Canada for the Red Cross, came and saw my pet while she was at Red Deer. A big party of Australian airmen came up from Calgary just to see him, and groups of English, Scottish, and Irish airmen from the R.A.F. training school at Penhold, eight miles from Red Deer, came to see him nearly every day, as well as soldiers from the

Army Service Corps camp at Red Deer. Tourists visiting Red Deer always seemed to hear about Mickey and came to see him. All the members of the Elgar Junior Choir of Vancouver once came to see Mickey while I was sick in bed with rheumatic fever. They went out on the lawn and sang some lovely songs to cheer me up. So did the Innisfail Brownie Pack when they came from Innisfail, about twenty miles away.

A great many other visitors came to our home to have a look at a tame beaver. Morning, noon, and night, Dad and Mother and I were kept busy – on many Sundays and holidays, well over a hundred people came to our home to have a look at Mickey.

Only one man was angry with us. "You shouldn't have a beaver as a pet," he said. "Beavers belong to all the people of Canada, and you have no right to keep this animal away from the wilds."

He frightened me, and, although I was twelve years old at the time, I began to cry. My Dad told the man that he had talked to the Mounted Police about Mickey, and the police had given us permission to look after him. But this visitor kept insisting that we were breaking the law and said that Mickey should be taken out to the wilds and released. Dad tried to explain to him that our pet beaver wouldn't know how to look after himself in the wilds after being raised as a pet.

"Well, I'm going to report you to the authorities," said the man as he left.

We were all very worried about this, but when some of our

friends heard about it they spoke to Mr. David Ure, Minister of Agriculture in the Alberta Government. Mr. Ure explained the situation to Premier E. C. Manning, asking if it were not possible for our family to have some sort of written permission, so that we would not be bothered again by cranks. Mr. Manning wrote me a very nice letter, appointing me Mickey's official guardian and telling me that I could keep the beaver just as long as I wished. After that, whenever any visitor wondered about the official status of Mickey as a beaver protected by the laws of Canada, we just got out Premier Manning's letter and proved that we had permission to keep him as our pet.

This was the only unpleasant happening in all our long years of looking after dear Mickey, with over 20,000 people visiting him.

One of my Dad's favourite stories happened when Mother and I had gone away for a holiday and left Mickey in Dad's care. The first evening, when Mickey came in from the garage and discovered that I wasn't at home, he paddled quickly all through the house in a panic, mewing loudly. My Dad talked to him and petted him, but at that moment Mickey wanted me. Again and again he wandered through the house, going from room to room in the downstairs part before climbing up the stairs, his big tail thumping noisily at every step. All the time, he kept mewing or wailing.

"Then something happened," Dad told us, after we got home.

"I'd left Mickey in the front room, crying his heart out, and I'd gone to the kitchen to make myself a cup of coffee and had almost given up hope of getting him calmed down. Suddenly his wailing stopped and I heard a scratching noise. I sat still for a moment, sipping my coffee, but that scratching sound made me curious. So I went out to the front hall to see what he was up to. There he was, stretched as tall as he could reach, his front paws scratching the wall under the coat-hooks where we keep some of our clothes. Right away I saw what he wanted – he was trying to reach your sweater, Doris, and it was just about six inches beyond his best stretch."

It was an old sweater, one that I had often worn while playing with Mickey outdoors. Probably my scent was on it, which is what caught Mickey's attention at that lonely moment.

"Well, I handed it down to him," Dad said. "Mick pressed it firmly against his nostrils. He was sitting on his hindquarters at the time, balanced on his big tail. Right away he began rocking his body back and forth as he hugged the sweater. From then on, Doris, all the time you were away, Mickey wouldn't let that sweater out of his sight or reach. He even carried it to bed with him. And, while he was still lonely for the whole of your holiday, he seemed to get a lot of comfort out of having the sweater near him, just to remind him of you."

Mickey became a local hero during the two summers of 1943 and 1944, when he was shown at the Red Deer Summer Fair.

The Women's Auxiliary wanted to raise extra funds to buy treats to send to the men of our district who were serving overseas in the war, and they asked our family's permission to set up a side-show tent and put Mickey on display. My own brother Jack was overseas at the time, so Dad and Mother and I were very happy to agree to this new idea. The Auxiliary charged ten cents admission for everyone entering the tent to see Mickey, and we arranged things so that either my Dad or Mother or I was always on hand to look after Mickey. Six thousand people visited him at those two summer fairs, and in this way a Canadian beaver raised $600 to help send food parcels to Red Deer men overseas.

After the war, when our little town of 3,000 people began to grow very quickly, Mickey seemed to have just as many visitors as before. One June day in 1946, Lady Olave Baden-Powell, the World Chief of the Girl Guides, came to see him. She seemed to be completely fascinated by dear Mickey and spent two hours with us, playing on the lawn with Mickey and me and following us along the banks of Waskasoo Creek. Some of her official party became rather alarmed, thinking that Lady Baden-Powell had become lost. But Mother just smiled and pointed to some willows down by the stream. There they found us, with the World Chief Guide carrying big, heavy Mickey because he was tired of walking!

Later, Kerry Wood's wife Marjory told us that when Lady Baden-Powell returned to Red Deer during the autumn of 1955, at the luncheon held in her honour, she said:

"It might be thought very strange that one should remember a city because of an animal, but that is how I remember your town – because I spent such a happy time here nine years ago with young Doris Forbes and her wonderful pet, Mickey the beaver!"

The main part of Red Deer is in a pleasant valley which at one time had a vast network of beaver canals and lodges where over a hundred animals lived before settlers came. Visitors to town would be shown all our new industries and new stores, the lovely old houses on residential streets, and the scenic parks; and then they'd be taken for a drive along the Red Deer River. Each tour included a stop at our home, where the strangers were introduced to my Dad and Mother and Mickey and me.

"I don't know why everybody wants to pick him up," Mother once said to me after we'd had a visitation of out-of-town guests. "When you meet a family's dog, you're quite content to pat the animal on the head and let it go at that. But when it comes to meeting Mickey everybody asks permission to pick him up and hold him for a moment. Perhaps they want to be able to go home and tell their families that they've actually handled a real live beaver!"

By this time Mickey was getting to be quite an armful. He weighed well over seventy pounds during the last few years of his life, and looked much larger than any of the wild beavers we saw swimming along Waskasoo Creek near by.

Thousands and thousands of people picked Mickey up, and not once did he show the slightest sign of crankiness towards anyone. Often he was sleepy in the middle of the day and wanted to climb back into his dark kennel to get out of the bright sunshine, but if we coaxed a little he didn't mind spending a few minutes meeting any new visitor who happened to come along.

Most visitors liked to feed him, and we soon learned that

shelled garden peas were perhaps Mickey's all-time favourite food. He never did learn how to shell the peas for himself, and Dad or Mother or I did that chore for him. Or we'd let the visitor shell a few peas and Mickey would mew happily, clutching the little peas in his paws and nibbling on them while he posed for still another picture.

During 1946 a Canadian publishing company began preparing a new reader to be used in the Grade IV classrooms of Canada. The book was titled *Up and Away,* and Kerry Wood was asked to send in an article about Mickey and me. As soon as the reader reached the classrooms and pupils began reading the story about Mickey, our mail-box and Kerry's became crowded with letters. My letters asked what Mickey liked to eat, how old was he now, and how old was I. Kerry often got as many as 400 or 500 letters during a single school term. He liked reading the letters. A girl named Sally, in Grade IV somewhere in eastern Canada, ended her list of questions to him: "With all my love!" One boy asked Kerry: "How much would Mickey's fur be worth if he were skinned?" That question made me feel quite sad.

After I finished school, I became a nurse-receptionist in Red Deer. I used to enjoy walking from home to the office with Tweed, our friendly big collie, running beside me to make sure I had a guardian all the way. And when I returned home from work at the end of the day I'd get a tumultuous welcome from

dear Mickey. I'm sure that Mickey loved all members of our family, but he seemed to have a special fondness for me because of the long hours we had spent together while he was growing up. By this time Mickey was moving slowly and aging, and his muzzle whiskers were quite grey. Yet he was as playful as ever. Each night he was brought into the house to spend some time with the family. When our bedtime came, Mickey would waddle contentedly back to the garage with one of us going along to close the doors and say "Good night". Sometimes we'd watch him by flashlight, as he inspected his stock of fresh poplar and willow logs, his big water pan, and extra food in the way of apples or whatever happened to be in season. He would busy himself out there in the garage all night long at beaver-work. Then, just at dawn, he would take his favourite pillow – my old sweater – and carry it into his warm kennel to sleep away the daylight hours.

One March morning in 1948 Dad and I walked towards town together, he to his railway engineer's job and I to the doctor's office, with big Tweed trotting beside us as our escort. Back at home, Mother washed the breakfast dishes and then went to the garage around nine o'clock to look in on Mickey. This was a morning ritual with her; she just wanted to make sure he was all right. Usually she'd go into the garage, reach into his kennel, and give him a little pat on the head before closing the doors again and returning to the house.

On that particular morning, when she opened up the garage she saw that Mickey had enjoyed a busy night. He had piled

poplar and willow logs across the garage floor in the shape of a beaver-dam. He had eaten most of the carrots we had put out for him the night before, and he had chewed some fresh bark from the young willows Dad had cut for him from the banks of Waskasoo Creek. Mother saw that he had visited his water pan several times, and had splashed half of the water out of the container. Over in the far corner, he had piled up more logs and some old pieces of two-by-four lumber in the shape of a beaver's stick-lodge.

At dawn he had gone to his kennel. When Mother called to him, Mickey didn't answer with the little mew he usually sounded. She spoke his name again, and when he failed to answer her second call she bent down to look into the kennel. Mickey had used my old sweater as his pillow once again, and some time during his sleep he had died.

We were a sad family that day. My Dad made a wooden casket and dug a grave for him in a corner of the lawn where we had spent so many pleasant hours with him. Although we missed him a great deal in the days and weeks and months that followed, we remembered that he had been a very happy animal all through the nine years he had been with us.

THAT'S OUR CHEEP

THAT'S OUR CHEEP

Cheep came to us on a sunny mid-June morning, a very sick little robin. Some boys had found a nestful of fledglings in a boulevard tree and ripped it down. Three of the four young robins in it were brutally killed on the spot, and Cheep was thrust into a jacket pocket of one of the culprits, for disposal later. A girl who had seen the nest-raiding episode from her house window rushed out and insisted that the boy give her the only live robin left of the family.

She knew that, at our home, we often doctored sick or injured birds and animals. She brought the listless, half-dead birdling to us during the noon-hour break from school when our three children were at home. We keep an emergency kit on hand for treatment of wild creatures, the main item being a mixture of brandy and water with an eye-dropper to squirt the stimulant down the throat of a patient. This speeds up the heart action of a bird and helps it get over the shock of an injury. It was strongly recommended to us by an experienced veterinarian. The little robin was quickly given a shot of this brandy-water mixture. At once he raised up his head, shook it vigorously, and squawked:

"CHEEP!"

"Well, that can be his name," said my daughters Rondo and Heather, while my son Greg hustled to the garage to get the fork and dig for worms.

Cheep proved to be famished. Because he was still very young, we had to chop the worms into small fragments and thrust them deep down into his yellow-lined throat with round-nosed tweezers. He began fluttering his half-formed wings and cheeping loudly as he gulped this food, accepting piece after piece. We knew that it was impossible to over-feed a young robin, because a bird of this species becomes sleepy as soon as it has eaten enough. Eventually Cheep was satisfied. With a final little chirp, the bird hunched down in Rondo's hand and went to sleep.

By this time school bells were ringing in the town valley, and our three children had to hurry away. My wife Marjory and I

considered where we should keep our new patient. The youngsters' old play-house, located in trees north of the house, had been converted into a bird and animal hospital and there were two or three cages in it. However, neighbours' cats were always hanging around that little building, hopeful of catching one of our patients. When Cheep arrived, the play-house hospital happened to be empty, but when we looked that way we saw a grey tabby cat with its green eyes fixed upon the small, helpless robin.

"How about the sleeping-porch, upstairs?" suggested Marjory.

We placed Cheep in a roomy cardboard box, with a wadding of old woolly rags in a corner. Cheep was missing the close bodily contacts he'd had with his fellow nestlings and pressed tight against the cloths for warmth. We put him in a sunny corner of the eight-by-twelve-foot sleeping-porch, then I returned to the garden to dig a supply of worms while Marjory went down-town to buy hamburger.

Before she returned, Cheep was chirping loudly and was quite hungry again. Parent robins feed their fledglings every three minutes during the early stages of growth. We could not hope to devote so much time to our new patient, and had to rely on larger feedings at longer intervals. He was gulping down portions of worm when Marjory got back from town and asked:

"Shouldn't you wash the worms?"

I explained that the young robin's digestive system needed the roughage of the bits of earth which clung to the worms.

Marjory took over the feeding of Cheep during the school hours of that afternoon and soon learned that he needed a good filling every fifteen to twenty minutes. She varied his diet a little, offering small portions of raw hamburger and sometimes fragments of bread soaked in milk. Cheep accepted all offerings; by this time he was quite used to us and gaping his beak whenever he was hungry.

When the children came home, it was Heather who took over the feeding chores. Rondo was then in high-school and had to do more studying, while Heather had more free time. She was used

to handling worms, having helped gather them on numerous other occasions to feed injured gulls, robins, and blackbirds we had nursed back to health. One time a pair of young great horned owls was brought to us late at night when all stores were closed, and we had no raw meat in the house except a pound of bacon. Those ravenous owls ate all the lean bacon and yelped for more. Using flashlights, we went to the garden and dug up a double handful of worms for them. Rondo, Heather, and Greg still remembered that midnight feeding and how the owls squawked as they were fed lowly worms, but at least our children had learned not to be frightened of squirming worms.

"He ate six, last feeding," Heather told us at supper-time. "I timed him between feedings, and we'll have to try to give him food every thirteen minutes to keep him happy."

A water-dish in his box was just a nuisance at this stage, because Cheep did not know how to drink. He got liquids from the moist worms or in feedings of bread dipped in milk. And on very hot days we gave him squirts of water with the eye-dropper which he seemed to enjoy throughout his feeding-time.

After supper, Heather gave up her outdoor play-time to stay in the sleeping-porch with Cheep, feeding him whenever he was hungry and cuddling him in her hands between feedings.

"He's feeling the cold," she told us. "It's going to rain tonight and the air is cold. I noticed that Cheep is shivering."

At this end of a dismal day, it seemed wise to give the orphaned bird yet another dose of the warming brandy-water mixture.

Once again the young robin shook its head vigorously, opened its eyes widely, and chirped:

"CHEEP! CHEEP!"

However, the medicine helped. Cheep roused enough to gobble eight worms in chopped fragments. He refused more, uttering a soft, pleasing little note of contentment as he settled back into the woolly cloths in the box. We had changed these

three times, because of droppings. Parent robins always carry this refuse away from the nest. Now we had a clean, artificial nest for the young robin in a corner of the box, and as twilight came on we closed the lid and left him to sleep.

This happened around the middle of June, when the daylight period in our part of Alberta lasted until ten o'clock at night or later. The dawn came early, too – at a quarter to four next morning, to be exact. At that time Cheep chirped with ever-increasing loudness from his box on the sleeping-porch. I arose and fed him seven small gobs of hamburger dipped in milk, plus one chopped worm. No sooner had I fallen asleep again, about fifteen minutes later, than Cheep began chirping loudly and wanted a second helping. He got it, too. Our children slept soundly at this period and rarely heard Cheep during the dawn hours, but he could always coax Marjory or me from bed, time after time, when daylight came.

Cheep grew bigger and soon did not wish to remain squatted on the woolly rags in a corner of the box. He was ready to hop around, even though his wings were undeveloped and his feathering not yet complete. At night he perched on a branch we wedged across one corner of the box. During the day, he wanted more space than the confined range of the cardboard box, so we moved a table and chair and magazine racks out of the sleeping-porch. We left a wooden bench in the porch area, and Cheep tried and tried again to get up onto that bench. His wings would not help

him as yet, but sometimes Rondo, Heather, or Greg lifted the little bird onto the bench and Cheep perched happily on the seat, surveying the green leaves of balsam, poplar, Manitoba maple and lilac, and the darker fronds of spruce. Whenever a wild bird paused on any of the branches outside the screened porch, Cheep would instantly hush and intently watch it.

Sometimes adult robins saw the young, speckle-breasted orphan behind the sleeping-porch wire. Occasionally they uttered alarm notes, and on at least one occasion an adult robin landed on the edge of the porch and peered in at our patient.

"Maybe a pair would adopt him," suggested Rondo.

Marjory and I did not believe this was very likely, but young Greg became hopeful. He was getting tired of digging for worms in all the moist corners of the garden! In addition to raw hamburger, chopped worms, and bread and milk, Cheep was now getting fragments of ripe strawberries – at forty-nine cents a basket. He enjoyed the fruit, which we fed to him in cut-up portions half a dozen times a day.

Either Marjory or I fed the bird during school hours, and one of the three children took over feeding chores the rest of the time. Heather spent more time with him than the others, and Cheep became her special charge.

A spell of cold rainy weather set in towards the end of June, and this posed a problem. Should we bring Cheep into the house at night, or leave him in his box out on the sleeping-porch? The family opposed me for my heartlessness, but I insisted that he

should be left outside to hasten the growth of his blue-quilled and sprouting feathers.

They called me "Meany", yet Cheep did adorn himself with more and more feathers. One of my zoology text-books claimed that a robin is covered with a total of 2,500 feathers, counting small down feathers as well as stiff wing and tail plumes. Cheep grew his full assortment, and the effort made him hungrier than ever and his meals became larger.

"He ate nine worms this time," Heather reported at lunch-time.

"Wait!" interrupted her mother. "Please, go wash your hands before you sit down!"

"And he's eating them whole now," Heather added.

"Golly," murmured Greg. "Y'know, I wish we didn't have spaghetti for lunch today!"

Rondo was busier than ever with her books as final exams started for her grade. Heather, however, was excused from school in order that junior grades would be out of the way while the seniors wrote their exams. Greg, to his great disgust, was kept in class until the very end of the month.

"You can take over all the daylight feedings," Marjory told Heather. "Dad or I will look after the early morning jobs until you wake up, but the rest of the time Cheep is your baby."

"That's fine," Heather said, and two days later she proudly informed us at bed-time that she had put Cheep on a straight worm diet for that day and he had eaten 218 worms!

"That reminds me, I must scrub the porch floor again tomorrow," exclaimed Marjory, and the floor certainly needed cleaning every day.

By this time, the other young robin fledglings were chirping here and there on our lawn or in the back garden or over in neighbours' yards. We thought that Cheep should be getting more outdoor exercise, so Heather carried him down from the sleeping-

porch and onto the back lawn several times a day. The weather was still cool and rainy, which did not bother Cheep during the daytime. In fact, he appeared to enjoy feeling the rain on his feathers and began huffling them, trying to have a shower-bath.

This behaviour prompted us to place a shallow pie-pan filled with water on the porch floor. Cheep occasionally sat in the middle of the pan, chirping noisily but unable to bathe himself at this stage. He liked having Heather flick a few drops over his plumage, whereupon he would huffle himself and preen his feathers with his beak. After every wetting, he felt the cold. At such times he liked to be held snugly in Heather's hands, enjoying the warmth of her fingers pressed close against his feathers. Whenever he felt the cold and any member of the family was feeding him, Cheep got into the habit of snuggling into our hands for warmth. It was not sanitary to hold him for long and there were many accidents. However, by using more of the woolly rags, we kept Cheep reasonably comfortable during this cold-weather period until the sun shone warmly again.

By that time, June had ended and Rondo was through with her exams and young Greg had been given his final report card.

"I passed, Family!"

We had owned a car for less than a year and it had been our hope to go on a family holiday to Banff when school was out. However, we could not leave Cheep alone.

"I'll take him outdoors more often, now that it's warm again," Heather said. "Maybe he'll learn how to hunt for his own food."

Most of the time, Cheep was content to sit on the grass somewhere near Heather, fluffing out his feathers to enjoy the warmth and starting his insistent "cheep" note whenever he got hungry. As his hunger increased, he would hop close to Heather and open his beak and beg to be fed.

"He's stupid," Heather told us at noon-time. "A perfectly good ant crawled right over his left toe, and Cheep looked down at it and watched it all the while with one eye, but he didn't offer to peck at it. I don't think he wants to learn how to feed himself."

"Well, strawberries were reduced to thirty-nine cents a box today," said Marjory. "I guess we can get him some as a special treat, and perhaps that will let you ease up on the worms for a bit."

"You miss the point, Mom," said Heather. "I *want* him to get independent. If he doesn't learn to feed himself soon, we'll never get a holiday."

One morning while Heather had Cheep under the platform-feeder where we keep bread-crumbs and table scraps and lumps of suet to feed birds, Cheep had a frightening experience.

"I keep hoping one of the adult robins will adopt him," Heather had said, and she noticed one young robin of Cheep's size under the feeder. She went close with our bird and placed him only four feet from the other fledgling. A moment later the

mother robin arrived on the scene with a beakful of worms to feed her young one.

"Cheep kept real quiet," Heather told us. "He hunched down there and watched, while I was back at the kitchen door watching too. I hoped that maybe she'd keep a piece of worm to feed him, then raise him as one of her own."

Instead, once she had poked the beakful of worms down the gaping throat of her own young, the mother robin swiftly turned and hopped toward Cheep and proceeded to peck him.

"You could almost hear Cheep yelling ouch!" said Heather. "She really hurt him, and there's a little blood near his beak where she stabbed him. All he did was rear back and open his beak and squawk, but she kept right on beating him up until I ran close and shooed her away and picked Cheep up."

Why had the mother robin attacked him? Perhaps there was something about Cheep's manner or behaviour that bothered her; perhaps she instinctively sensed that he was not a fully wild robin and had been raised by those bird-enemies, humans. In any case, whatever the reason for the attack, this thrashing set back Cheep's independence by at least a week. Heather took him outdoors half a dozen times every morning and afternoon, coaxing him to become his own boss. She placed worms on the grass near him. Cheep eyed them with what appeared to be intelligent interest, but he did not make any attempt to pick them up. At this stage of his development, food was simply not known as food unless it was thrust well down his throat.

"I think he's a bird moron," Heather said crossly at suppertime. "A dozen times I've put worms down in front of him and he won't touch them. But every time my hand or fingers get near him, he opens up his beak and begs for food. He considers me to be his maw."

"Hi, Maw!" Rondo grinned.

"It isn't funny," retorted Heather. "When will we get our holidays?"

"Oh, let's not get excited," Marjory comforted her. "Just keep taking Cheep outdoors, and one of these days he'll fly off and leave you."

By this time Cheep could fly for short distances. He would no longer stay inside the cardboard box at night. The box had been removed from the sleeping-porch and Cheep was given the full run of that region. Most of the time he spent on the bench seat, or on the linoleum-covered floor itself – and, once, I had seen him try to capture a small and nimble fly that buzzed past his head. Every evening after his final feeding of worms, strawberries, hamburger, and bread and milk Cheep flew from the porch floor onto the seat of the bench. There he tried, often inexpertly, to go for another short flight that would carry him up to the back of the bench. It was part of the bird's instinct to seek the highest possible perch at night, safely away from the ground where there might be prowling cats and other enemies. We often glanced out at him after dark, and would see Cheep with his head tucked underneath a wing, fast asleep on the top bar of the bench-back.

How did the bird manage to stay on the perch, after it was fast asleep? Perching birds have special locking muscles that keep their claws firmly on a branch once they have settled down for the night.

Next morning, Heather was radiant when she came in from the lawn with Cheep on her wrist.

"He ate an ant!" she announced triumphantly. "It started to crawl past him, and Cheep spotted it and took a hop or two, then he reached out and grabbed the ant and swallowed it. He's learning!"

He ate unidentified insects on three different occasions during

that special, red-letter day. Better still, when Heather deposited a worm on the grass in front of him Cheep reached out and grabbed it and, after two tries, managed to gulp down the wriggling food.

"Can we go to Banff tomorrow, Dad?" asked Greg.

"Well-l-l-l, not yet, but soon."

"It all depends on Heather and Cheep," said Marjory.

Rain or shine, Heather took Cheep outdoors a dozen times the next day. She would rush excitedly into the house to announce that Cheep had eaten a black beetle, a small centipede, or another ant. She wasn't feeding him worms from her fingers or tweezers any longer; she placed them on the ground or porch floor in front of Cheep and waited until the hungrily chirping robin helped himself.

Two days later, with many more reports of self-feedings, Heather came charging into the house and demanded that we all come outdoors at once. Cheep had been startled by the sudden appearance of Skippy, the friendly spaniel from next door, and had flown from the lawn and landed on a maple branch at least eight feet up from the ground.

"He can fly!" Heather insisted. "Dad, he can look after himself okay now, so we really could go to Banff tomorrow."

But Cheep had other ideas. He hopped down to the ground, ran quickly across the lawn, then gaped his beak in Heather's direction and out came that distinctive, well-known sound:

"CHEEP!"

"Feed him, Maw," Rondo teased.

"Aw, gee!" Heather muttered, but she went for the worm-can and poked in a finger to expose one of the crawlers, which she dropped on the ground in front of the robin. Cheep pounced on it at once, swallowed it, and gaped his beak for more. Heather poked a finger here and there in the can, then handed it to Greg.

"Here, Greg – more worms, please."

"Gee whizz!" said the boy, going for the fork once again.

A kindly farmer and his family heard of our problem of hand-raising a robin and almost exhausting our garden's supply of worms. He drove into our lane that afternoon and handed us a jam-tin literally packed with worms.

"A present for Cheep," he smiled, and he and his wife and little girls watched with interest while Heather gave the young robin yet another hearty feeding.

At the end of that day, Heather tried to persuade us that Cheep was ready to spend the night outdoors on his own. Since the bird was perched contentedly on her arm at the moment, it did not seem the proper time to take him outside and turn him loose in the cat-infested neighbourhood. Once again, Heather climbed the stairs and went to the sleeping-porch, where Cheep hopped from her arm onto the back of the bench, uttered the pleasant little note which indicated he was well satisfied with life, then promptly tucked head under wing and fell asleep.

Next morning at four o'clock, my slumbers were shattered once more by the loud and insistent calls from the porch near by, and

our robin was given an assortment of worms, pieces of bread and milk, fragments of hamburger, and some diced strawberries Marjorie had placed in readiness the night before. At twenty-minute intervals until breakfast-time, either Marjory or I had to feed the hungry Cheep until Heather woke up.

"Hi, Maw – guess who wants you?"

"I'm going to take him outside right away," Heather said. "He's getting himself a complex, or something. He's just got to learn to look after himself, and soon."

"Yeah, it's two whole weeks past our holiday-time now, Mom," protested Greg.

"You'd better un-complex him then, Maw," Rondo smiled, as Heather carried Cheep outdoors and forced him to scrounge part of his meal from the numerous crawly things available on the ground underneath the feeder-platform.

When she came in for her own breakfast, she told us that she had left Cheep on the feeder-platform where we could all see him from the dining-room windows.

"He ate a couple of ants and a little brown bug and two or three other things I couldn't see, then I gave him five worms. He's full to the gills now, and he can just sit there a while and think about life, time, and space as it concerns robins!"

Cheep was developing rapidly, helped by Heather's insistence on his independence. More and more often he hopped this way and that when on the lawn or in the garden, pecking at various

insects and tiny creatures we could not see. Once we saw him cock his head on one side in the typical attitude of an adult robin listening for a worm moving amidst the grassroots. But as yet, Cheep had not dug out a worm for himself.

About this time, Cheep became known to all of Canada, at least, to all of those people who were listening to the CBC's Trans-Canada radio network. A radio engineer friend of mine, Ken Martin, agreed to bring a portable recording-machine to our home and set it up in the kitchen and let me take the microphone on a long cord out on the back porch. We recorded Cheep's melodious chirps and appreciations for his snack of six or seven servings of strawberries and bread and milk. This brief recording was later released in the weekly series I was doing for the radio network at that time, along with some pertinent facts about Cheep.

Skippy, the spaniel, came over to our yard several times a day. On each visit, Cheep uttered an alarm note and flew to the nearest branch. The bird was demonstrating more ability at flying, and one afternoon Heather called us out to show us that Cheep had reached a tree-perch at least twenty feet above the ground.

"Now can we go to Banff?" she asked.

That same night Cheep protested at being cooped in the sleeping-porch; he wanted a much higher perch than the back of the bench. We carried him outdoors and set him high on a spruce branch, well out of reach of cats. At dawn I heard his

clamorous appeals for food and went to the back porch to give him raw hamburger.

"Go scrounge something for yourself now," I suggested before going back to bed.

Cheep must have followed this advice, because he did not

yelp for food for nearly an hour. All that day and the next, we could see that he was becoming more sure of himself. He still liked to come to the back porch and have a bath in the pie-pan, and he loved strawberries – now twenty-nine cents a basket, which allowed the family to share them. He was fully grown and sassy-natured now, a strong flier and fully alert to all the dangers around him, including Skippy, the skulking cats in the underbrush – even the neighbourhood children taking a short-cut through our yard. All such things sent Cheep flying up to a high and safe perch. He trusted no humans but ourselves and, remembering what had happened to his nest-mates, we were pleased to note this trait.

With saskatoon berries ripe and purple just beyond the front lawn and robins feasting on them from morning to night, and an abundance of creepy insects on the ground to provide rich fare for dozens of young robins that had been independent of their parents a matter of weeks, we finally decided it was safe to leave on our holiday.

Yet we were worried as we loaded up the tiny car with foodstuffs and clothing and camping gear, ready to leave for Banff. Heather was tearful at the end, quite remorseful about her own hard-heartedness during the past few days that had forced Cheep to become independent of our care. With everything loaded and ready, we arranged the back porch so that it had an ample supply of cut strawberries and ripe saskatoon berries, portions of raw

hamburger, a bowl of bread and milk, two pie-pans full of bath water, and a new supply of food out on the feeder-platform in case he paid it a visit. Cheep was given a feeding of nine worms, then he flew into a poplar tree and settled himself on a sunny perch for a morning snooze.

"Good-bye, Cheep," said Greg, and our small boy sounded husky.

Rondo and Heather both wept openly as we drove out of the yard, whereupon Marjory asked them if they really wished to call off the holiday.

"Oh, go ahead, now that we've started," Heather sobbed.

"And he'll never learn any younger," Rondo agreed.

They were a quiet trio of children for the first ten miles of our 200-mile drive to Banff. This was our first family visit to the famous mountain resort and there was much for us to see and enjoy. But, every time a robin flew within sight, a noticeable silence settled upon the three youngsters on the back seat. On the fourth morning away from home, mid-way through our expected holiday-time, Heather suggested that we'd had enough of Banff and perhaps we should go home, please.

"I'm worried sick about Cheep," she confessed, and Rondo and Greg quickly sided with her.

We packed the car and left Banff. Coming into our home town of Red Deer, there was an uneasy silence among the children. They were really frightened as we finally turned in at our own lane and drove to the garage and stopped the car.

Heather was the first out, calling, "Here, Cheep! Come, Cheep!"

At once there was an explosion of wings from a tree to the north and a lusty, loud clamouring from a healthy-looking robin. Cheep flew at once to Heather and landed on her shoulder. His beak gaped wide open.

"Hurry!" she shouted happily. "Get the keys and open the garage and we'll dig some worms."

Cheep did not have to wait long. He was content with bread and milk, which we had in the car and could prepare in a rush.

"Aw, gee!" said Heather, smiling from ear to ear.

"He's a beautiful bird," said Rondo, coaxing him to take one more lump of milk-soaked bread.

"Can I get him a worm now?" asked Greg.

We made no attempt to keep the robin penned after that. He had the run of the yard but he would come whenever any member of the family called, willing to accept whatever food titbit we offered, though he was obviously well able to find his own meals now. His own particular delight was the pie-pan full of water on the back porch, where he had many a vigorous, wing-splashing bath in the refreshing water put out for him. It did not matter to the bird if the pan happened to be in our hands when we called him to have a bath. Often he took the bath before we could set the pan on the porch, and whoever was holding the dish usually got well drenched from all his splashings.

The closest part of our friendship with him came to an end on the day a family of friends paid us a visit. Cheep had never trusted any strangers, and this all-day visit ended his tame period.

He would stay on the tree-tops near by and answer our calls with his special whistle, and we often saw him come to the back porch to bathe in the pan or to pick up pieces of strawberry or freshly soaked bread and milk. But never again did he come directly to us after the presence of strangers all one day in the house and yard.

When autumn came, he was the last robin to leave us. October was nearly spent and all other robins in the district had flown south, while Cheep still feasted on our sand-cherries, mountain ash berries, Opata plums, crab-apple seeds, and any other fruit he could find in the garden. We saw him searching for the plentiful snow-berries and wolf-berries on the wild hill-side near by, and occasionally he would pluck dried saskatoons off twigs in the grove near the front lawn. Daily we put out bread and suet and crushed wheat and seed fare – also some dried currants. Cheep became a regular visitor to the feeder-platform and seemed especially fond of ground suet.

One dark and cloudy night the snow started falling for the third time that autumn. There was an ominous chill in the air and a rising howl to the wind that drove the small, stinging sleet-flakes. By morning, the ground was covered with eight inches of closely packed snow.

Cheep was nowhere to be seen, though we searched his favourite haunts for any glimpse of him or of his tracks. I was privately fearful that I might find his frozen body on the ground under the central maple tree, which had become his favourite perching place. But there was no trace of our robin.

When the March thaw arrived, the first robin back in our yard was the fully matured, plump-breasted Cheep. His breast feathers were a brilliant orange and his head-cap a glossy black, and he always seemed much more colourful to us than any other robin. Cheep whistled to us from tree-top positions and was willing to alight on the feeder-platform or come to the back porch when it was deserted to partake of any food-offerings we put out for his use. However, he refused to come to our hands, though the children coaxed him again and again.

He won a mate, and they raised a family of four on one of the robin-shelves within view of our dining-room. Cheep proved to be a good parent, industrious and alert. He called loud alarms whenever a cat came into the yard and we felt he was grateful when we rushed out to shoo cats away from his brood of little ones. He took charge of his four fledglings when they left the nest, fussing over the speckle-breasted young and feeding them a variety of wild fare and foodstuffs from our feeder. Meanwhile, his mate was busily incubating three more eggs in a second nest, this time built on a robin-shelf at the front part of the house.

Sometimes Cheep would follow Heather down through the

woodlands on trees near the short-cut path, answering her calls with his special whistle which we all knew so well. He stayed in or near our yard throughout that summer, and came back to raise his broods on house-shelves the next season, and the next. Heather thinks he is still coming back to our home grounds, and perhaps he is. Any time we see an extra-large male robin, and the bird responds to the calls we used so often during the June and July period when young Cheep was a helpless orphan, we smile at one another and say,

"That's our Cheep!"

THE BLIND DEER

THE BLIND DEER

It was near Red Deer, Alberta, in a game sanctuary that I saw my first wild deer. I had watched deer penned in zoos and glimpsed them from windows of speeding trains and cars, but, despite the abundance of their neat pointed tracks along creek and river shores near home, I had not been able to stalk deer in their own environment. Often when walking through the sanctuary I heard the bump-bumpity-bump of their bounding leaps,

but always the animals had taken fright and fled before I had a chance to sight them. Even in winter-time, when I saw their packed runways in the thick-wooded ravine between the two Gaetz Lakes where browse-food was plentiful, I was not able to see the wild deer.

In our part of Canada, if you wanted to have a picnic or a walk in the woodlands, the place to go was the sanctuary. We did not call it by the "sanctuary" name at first. Earlier it was known as Jack Gaetz's Lakes. There were two lakes on the 200-acre wilderness, though very few people walked past the first small thirty-acre pond just a quarter-mile from the main road on the northern outskirts of our town. Second Lake was well screened by noble old spruce trees and dense growing poplars and balms, while its shores and shallows were heavily grown to thick willows and tall bulrushes. That was where the nature students liked to go, because Second Lake provided such a large variety of water birds to see. And around both lakes, those who studied the occasional patches of sandy shore could always find the tracks of deer.

When I was sixteen years old, my boyhood days suddenly ended. My family had moved away and I embarked on a career as a writer. During the early struggle, hunger was my constant companion, because I was forced to live off the land. The summer was not too difficult while fish, berries, and edible plants were in abundance, but winters were lean and hungry seasons. During the second summer, I thought that if I could hunt a deer when the autumn big-game period fell due, I would have meat

enough to last part of the winter and help to vary my diet of rabbits, poplar bark, and porcupine flesh.

This decision to hunt deer sent me to the sanctuary, not to shoot, but to study deer tracks. I hoped to learn how to stalk those elusive animals, which lived in considerable numbers along the river wilds.

There I was on the shore of First Lake, sketching deer tracks grooved in the muddy sand near the creek mouth. Later I was to learn that I could not bring myself to shoot or kill anything so beautiful as a deer, but at that moment of summer I was busily drawing the track details when a quiet voice spoke behind me.

"What're you doing?"

It startled me to find an Indian standing near by, watching me with intent brown eyes. He had come close on his quiet moccasins and I had not heard his approach. Probably he was amused by my nervous jump, though his solemn expression did not reveal it. I showed him my track sketches and told him of my interest in learning how to stalk.

"Venison don't keep good in summer," he commented.

I explained that shooting a deer was not my immediate intention; indeed, my only weapon at the moment was a lead pencil. It was stalking that I wished to learn, to use this knowledge to hunt a deer when the legal shooting season opened in the late fall. In any case, I added, the Gaetz Lake woodlands were a wildlife sanctuary where hunting was strictly prohibited.

The Indian nodded, apparently satisfied about my motives. He

hunched down beside the marks on the sandy mud and proceeded to give me a practical lesson in track reading. Always look at them against the sun, he said. In so doing, kick-ups of earth or snow would show up in shadow and supply extra details of the animal's behaviour. The chief idea of looking at tracks was to find out what the animal had been doing when it printed the marks on the ground or snow. A tracker could tell at a glance if it was walking or running. If it was speeding, had it been frightened, and why? If not, where was it going? There were several possibilities: to get a drink, to seek food, or to find a refuge where it could hide or sleep in safety.

Once he was sure that all this was understood, the Indian pointed again at the tracks on the sands of the creek mouth and said, "These marks were made today, a few hours ago. At this hot time of early afternoon, deer lie down and rest. She won't be far away, so let's go find her."

He led the way through willows and black alder, along the banks of the creeklet that drained the topland. Now and then he pointed a bronzed finger at tracks that were occasionally clearly marked, at other times merely depressions in the grass. Occasionally he touched a branch of birch, drawing my attention to frayed ends of twigs on which the deer had browsed. He also showed me a spot where the animal had nuzzled a clump of clover and plucked a few mouthfuls of the tender leaves. All this time he was walking slowly and quietly through the creekside woods, and I did my best to stay close behind and to move silently.

Suddenly the Indian stopped. For a long time we stood motionless on the sun-dappled forest floor. He signalled for extreme caution; then we moved forward a few careful steps. He waited until I drew alongside him, then put his lips close to my ear, whispering, "We scared the doe from its day-bed. D'you see her?"

I stared at the area he indicated, roving my eyes over dense growth of willow and alder, noting the white sheen of a birch farther up the bank and the dark shadows of the green spruces which formed the ravine's backdrop. I looked again, searching the thickets with puzzled eyes. There were tiny mirrored flashes of sun on smooth willow leaves, other sparkles of reflection on the creek waters. Many of the stream-bed boulders were a dull grey in colour, others were mottled with browns and reds and the yellows of sandstone. An evening primrose was in bloom on one sandy gravel bar; above that blossom I stared intently at a tan blur beyond the far creek bank. At last this thing assumed the shape of a leaf-screened stump. But – I could not see any deer.

Sadly, I had to shake my head and the Indian once again leaned close to whisper, "Watch left of big stump."

Very slowly, he stooped to pick up a pebble. When the stone was in his hand, he flicked it across the creeklet. The pebble landed with a small but explosive sound, and there was a rustle of movement in the thicket.

There stood the deer!

"Oh, look!" I whispered excitedly. "She's a beauty!"

I turned to share my pleasure with my new friend and saw on his face a strange expression of wonder.

"Blind," he muttered.

At first I thought he was condemning my own inability to

locate the animal for myself, but another glance at his face made me turn to stare more closely at the deer. This time I noticed a milky film covering the doe's eyes, and with a catch of breath realized that she was completely sightless. After a moment's hesitation in full view of the Indian and me, the animal turned and cautiously felt her way through the tangle of willows to reach a hidden pathway beyond. Once on that trail, she went bounding along at full speed and soon passed from sight.

The Indian said something which I did not properly hear – something about the deer being touched by Gitchee-Manitou, the Great Spirit. I sensed his awe and reverence, and we were silent as we turned and walked back to the lake shore.

I sought her out many times after that initial meeting when the Indian taught me how to stalk. Before leaving me that day, he counselled me to take up a position in a well-screened hide near the creek ravine at either morning or evening and remain in hiding for an hour or more.

"Let the doe come to you. Pick a place downwind from where you think she may be resting in a day-bed. That way, she won't scent you and won't fear coming close. 'Nother thing: don't tell your friends about her. No Indian would shoot a blind animal but . . ."

He did not finish the sentence, yet I caught the meaning. A white man who was keen on venison might take advantage of the deer's affliction and try to bag himself an easy victim. Perhaps

so. And I respected the Indian's counsel about the need for secrecy regarding her presence in the near-home woodlands.

Nature had given her very acute hearing to compensate for her darkened eyes. She was never easily stalked, even after I became thoroughly familiar with her three-acre range. Most of it was in the thick cover of the creek ravine, where birch- and alder-browse was plentiful. There were clumps of grass at the edge of the stream bank, also beds of clover – the seeds having washed down from Jack Gaetz's pasture lands. There was no lack of food for her, either in winter or summer. After I put into practice the Indian's instructions about hiding and watching, I saw her often. I found her favourite drinking-hole about fifty feet away from a thick willow grove, where I could sit well back from her trail and wait for her coming at morning or evening. How I savoured the mounting tension, hearing the thump-thump of hooves as she came on the run, or the occasional thump of a single hoof if she browsed slowly along the path on her way to the spring for a drink.

One day I saw her running at full gallop with two tawny coyotes racing along a hundred feet behind her. I rushed close after the deer had passed, and the coyotes saw me at once. They skulked off into deep cover, going in the opposite direction. Perhaps she was safe enough from them, because coyotes are rarely bold enough to attack a fully grown deer. Had they sensed her handicap and hoped for an easy kill, or were they hoping that she might lead them to another prize which I did not know

about at that time? My intervention frightened them away, and I stayed there until the full moon rose above the hill-top spruces just in case they tried another stalk. The yapping call of the male coyote rose from the woodlands over on the far side of

Second Lake just as the doe came like a grey ghost through the dim shadows and lowered her muzzle to the water.

If I could not get a glimpse of her during a sanctuary visit, there were other things to reward me. On Second Lake, for example, a pair of marsh hawks had made a nest on top of a deserted muskrat house which was well screened by bulrushes. I loved to watch those harrier hawks, though sometimes the passing of the slim grey male would bring a bedlam of alarm notes from blackbirds, ducks, and coots. Even the tiny yellow warblers uttered a metallic chirp of anxiety when the hawk flew over. Perhaps the hunter would have accepted a bird-prize if given the chance, though any time I was watching the hawk was hunting for mice. Thick-growing slough grass fringing the lake harboured nests of meadow mice or Drummond's voles, while at the edge of the forest growth there were red-backed voles, the woodland variety of the meadow-mouse species. I often saw the grey male hawk fluttering its wings to hover in one place ten or fifteen feet above the ground. Then it dropped, sharp talons clutching at a grassy or leafy area and often closing on the body of a mouse.

One morning that same spring I made a wonderful discovery. In the soft mud at the creek mouth, the blind doe's neat prints had a set of very small prints alongside. She must have a fawn!

Despite my best efforts at stalking, I could not find her day-bed that day or the next. Several days passed before I gave up the search for the place where she hid the fawn and waited, as usual,

near the spring where she drank. The breeze was right, and my scent blew away from her coverts. Eventually she came along the trail she knew so well.

Ahead of her walked the fawn, a beautiful little stag still wearing the mottled garb of a very young deer. In some manner that fawn knew about the doe's blindness, because it acted as leader whenever they wandered through her secluded part of the sanctuary. The doe kept her muzzle near her young, nuzzling him gently from time to time but following trustfully wherever he led. She knew her own trails perfectly and ventured away from them only when the fawn led their feeding excursions. By this time he was cropping the tender grasses and leaves, though still nursing from her at intervals. And she was a most devoted mother.

All that summer and autumn, they were together and happy. They were still together for most of the winter, by which time the fawn was almost as large as its mother. Then I found a stale and snow-covered deer track half a mile to the north of the Gaetz Lakes near the river shore. This may have been the fawn's trail, printed when the time came for the natural parting of young from old. I felt very sorry for the doe, standing alone in her ravine thickets and turning her sightless eyes this way and that as nose and ears tested the signs that day and on many days to come. Her little one had grown up and gone; undoubtedly, she sorely missed his company. Once again, her range shrank to her original pathways and trails and feeding-places so familiar to her.

It became more difficult to stalk her after the fawn left and spring came. She seemed to stay in the denser thickets after that parting. Many times the woodland gossips gave away my hiding-place: the kakking of a magpie alerted the deer, and sometimes she heeded the persistent scold of a nesting blackbird or even the tirade of a red squirrel.

More interesting than the red squirrels were the shy animals of the night, the flying squirrels. They do not fly, of course; they glide from the tops of tall trees a distance of forty, fifty, even seventy feet, before ending the swoop across a clearing to flatten against the base of tree trunks on the far side. Many times, during evening watches at the blind doe's spring, I saw the swift passing of flying squirrels and heard their soft whistlings. Occasionally they raided the cone-caches of red squirrels, more often searching for insects resting on tree bark or hiding inside old woodpecker holes, and sometimes the sundown squirrels plucked a mushroom and carried it aloft to a tree perch to eat it.

Once I saw a great horned owl chase a flying squirrel. The panicked animal swooped from tree to tree, with the big owl following closely and trying to get a clear dive to close its talons on its prey. The squirrel raced up to the higher branches of a spruce, no doubt trying to find a hole or other safe refuge. But the owl circled the tree on soft-napped wings, repeatedly striking in among the needled branches. Out from the spruce-top came the squirrel, gliding again. This was the opportunity the owl wanted. Swiftly it dived on its intended victim. At the last pos-

sible instant, the squirrel reversed its direction and passed under the owl to reach the base of another tree. It was an old poplar stump with a deserted flicker-hole near the top. The squirrel disappeared into that black opening just as the owl swooped at it. The bird waited and waited, hooting at intervals, but the squirrel remained safely hidden.

One moonlit night later that spring, from the same woodpecker-hole, came a family group of five young flying squirrels. They were big-eyed and beautiful, all perched in a nervous row upon a branch arching out from the nest-hole where they had been born. Through the night woods came the mother, gliding to a sudden stop on the stump below them. What a joyous chorus of soft whistles greeted her, then all disappeared into the nest-hole to have supper. Later still, the family played a follow-the-leader game behind the mother, as she introduced them to the wide world of the night woods.

Next autumn, when poplar leaves were yellow, I went one Saturday afternoon to the sanctuary to have another look at the blind deer. There were gangs of boys in the Gaetz Lake woodlands that day, playing Indians and cowboys along the paths, and some were busy at lighting a camp-fire on the shore of First Lake and getting out wieners to roast. Their youthful shouts were loud, and I knew that the doe would stay in a hidden bed while the boys were there.

"What're yuh doing?" one asked me.

"Just watching the birds," I answered, pointing to the chicken-beaked coots rafted in mid-lake and a red-tailed hawk soaring high up against the pale blue sky. A migrant flock of siskins were cheeing in the spruce tops above the boys' fire, while back in the forest a young ruffed grouse was hesitantly trying out its drumming – not the brisk drumming challenge of spring-time, but the softer, uneven drumming of a learner. Another learner was there, a white-throated sparrow uttering those clear silvery notes a poet has interpreted as meaning, "Oh, Canada, Canada, Canada!"

The boys got on with their cooking while another gang shouted from the woodlands between the two lakes, and I hurried to the creek ravine, worrying in case they frightened the blind doe. By this time I knew her trails, though I could never fathom how she memorized them. Perhaps it was by scent, perhaps by a sense of touch such as the brush of a branch at one spot, or the contours of the ground warning her of turns and trees. Along certain routes she could run as fleetly as any normal deer, though whenever she left her known trails to seek browse-twigs she moved slowly and cautiously and was always ready to spring back to the path and run away from any threat of danger.

This day I took up a position in my hide near the spring hole. The boys who had been between the two lakes came hurrying back across the creek, because the cooks had shouted that the wieners were ready to eat. As the four husky youngsters came to the deer's trail, they paused to push on the stump of a dead

Balm of Gilead tree. They had to rock the stump a few times before the old roots loosened their long hold on the soil. But at last they made it crack, and down crashed the stump. The boys laughed over this feat of strength, then hustled towards the fire on the shore of First Lake.

Meanwhile, two boys not of their party had gone exploring up the creek ravine. I could hear their shouts and knew they were near the doe's probable day-bed. Suddenly I heard the thump-thump of her bounding gait. She was travelling the water-hole trail, one of her favourite pathways, on which she could speed. But – she slammed directly into the newly fallen stump and sprawled to earth. I had to hold myself still, resisting the impulse to rush forward and try to help her. A human's presence at such a time would have frightened her very badly, and this knowledge held me quiet.

I saw a violent trembling shudder through her body and realized the greatness of the shock she had suffered. Very slowly she climbed to her feet, then edged herself around the ten-foot log a few inches at a time. Once she was on the far side and again on her pathway, she took a tentative step or two, then she plunged forward in a bounding lope as the two boys farther up the ravine let out a shout about seeing a squirrel.

After the doe had passed from sight into the thickets near the lake, I rushed forward and lost no time hauling the old stump to one side. I dragged it well back from her path, placing it beside another deadfall about twenty paces from the deer's trail. It was

a wasted kindness. From then on, every time the blind doe came along that particular path, she made a careful detour around the area where the stump had caused her to fall. She took no second chance with the obstacle which was no longer there.

Winter came, and I saw her packed trails in the dense coverts of her ravine range. Snow provided her with drink, while food-twigs were in abundance for her to eat. The sanctuary was deserted in winter after snow covered First Lake ice and spoiled it for skaters, and usually I had the woodlands to myself. It was easier to stalk her then, as she could not hide behind leaves or hunch close to the forest floor and rely on shadows and her grey-brown coat for camouflage. I could sometimes see her from afar, body silhouetted against the white background of the snow. The coyotes left their dog-trails on her runways, but that did not bother me now after two years of knowing her. Once, in mid-winter I met a Canada lynx in the creek ravine woods with a dead rabbit clutched in its jaws. The lynx uttered a muffled snarl before it turned and went at an awkward-looking lope into spruce cover to have its meal. A twenty-pound lynx would never dare to tackle a 150-pound deer, so its presence there did not alarm me.

Snow was deep that winter, and in March her trails were narrow paths between yard-high drifts. I saw where she had pushed off the path to seek fresh browsing, but no other human tracks except my own were in the woodlands and I was careful to keep well back from her yards at that time. It was a delight to see her, still sleek and fair of body, still moving with that lovely grace which no other wild animal can equal. And this was to be my last look at her.

When the April thaw came there were no more fresh tracks, no signs at all. I went all through the creek ravine without finding

a single clue to the doe's whereabouts. Then I searched again, half expecting to find her body. I stopped and listened to the woodland gossips, but there was no gathering of magpies or jays, nor any coyote trail leading to a carcass.

I had guarded the secret of her presence too well, always fearful that someone might betray her to a hunter. That was my mistake; Sid and other friends could have shared my watch over the lovely animal, and one of them might have learned what finally became of her. In time other deer came to the sanctuary; two bull moose remained there one season and nearly ruined the water-lily patch with their feedings on the roots. But never again did I see the blind deer.

She was truly a queen of that forest, serene and much more graceful and beautiful than any other deer I saw in later years. Truly, as the Indian had said, she had been touched by the Great Spirit, and her loveliness remains as a benign spirit haunting the sanctuary that was her home.

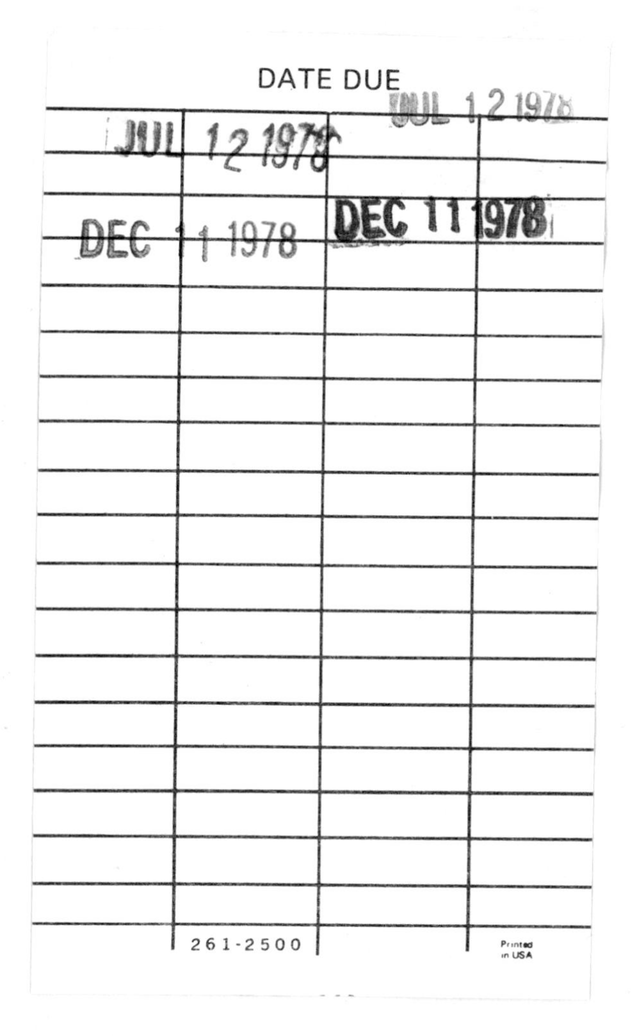
DATE DUE
JUL 12 1978
JUL 12 1978
DEC 11 1978
DEC 11 1978
261-2500
Printed in USA